Table of Contents

Why do we have zoos?

People have always been curious about wild animals. Many people have kept small wild animals as pets. Some people have even kept large animals such as lions and tigers.

A zoo is a place where all people can see many kinds of wild animals. The first zoo was started in Paris, France in 1804. Scientists could study wild animals at the Paris Zoo. Soon other cities built zoos. Zoos still have scientists. The scientists study the animals. Scientists make sure the animals have the right care. But the main purpose for zoos is so that people can see wild animals.

Zoos help people learn about wild animals. Zoos also help protect endangered species. If a species is "endangered," it means that there are not many of a certain kind of animal left in the world. Zoos give them a safe place to live and raise their young.

Why do we have zoos?

Underline another good title for this story.

Endangered Species

The First Zoo

<u>Why Zoos Are Important</u>

Underline the main idea of the story.

<u>Zoos help people see and learn about wild animals.</u>

The first zoo was in Paris, France in 1804.

Scientists study animals in the zoo.

Match.

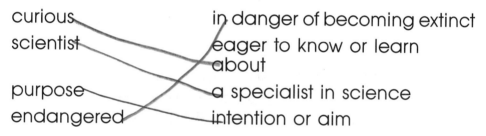

curious — in danger of becoming extinct

scientist — eager to know or learn about

purpose — a specialist in science

endangered — intention or aim

Circle.

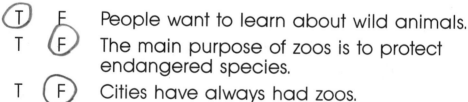

(T) F People want to learn about wild animals.

T (F) The main purpose of zoos is to protect endangered species.

T (F) Cities have always had zoos.

Check the three that apply.

Zoos . . .

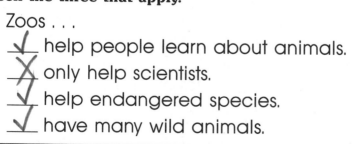

✓ help people learn about animals.

✗ only help scientists.

✓ help endangered species.

✓ have many wild animals.

3

What is a national park?

A national park is land that belongs to the public. The government provides roads into the national parks and places where people can have picnics. Many national parks have places where people can stay overnight. The government hires people to take care of the land. The government has laws that protect the wildlife in a national park. The government tries to preserve (keep) the natural beauty of the land.

Yellowstone Park was made a national park in 1872. It was the first national park in the world. Soon the government made other beautiful places into national parks. Congress also sets aside land for historical monuments. Now, we have around 300 national parks and monuments . The National Park Service was begun in 1916 to take care of all these places. The National Park Service is part of the government.

Underline another good title for this story.

The First National Park

Our National Parks

Overnight Campsites

Underline the main idea of the story.

Yellowstone was the first national park.

A national park is land that belongs to the public.
and its natural beauty is protected by the
government.

The National Park Service was begun in 1916.

Match.

provide   prevent from being harmed

preserve   to keep up; maintain

monument   make available

protect   something set up in memory of
                              a person or an event

Circle.

(T)   F   A national park belongs to everyone.

(T)   F   You can have a picnic at a national park.

(T)   F   Yellowstone is the oldest national park.

Check the two that apply.

The National Park Service . . .

✓ takes care of national parks.

✗ takes care of schools.

✓ takes care of historical monuments.

Why are museums important?

Museums are places where original objects are stored and displayed. Original means "not a copy." Original things are real. Some museums display works of art. They display art done by the artists. They do not display copies. Some museums display clothing, furniture, and other things that were used a long time ago. Things that were used by famous people are especially interesting.

Museums are important because they teach us about life and art forms of the past. Some museums display preserved animals and plants. Museum scientists are careful to show how these things really looked when they were alive. Some museums display famous things that are important to sports, music, science, and history. Some museums display things that have been used by people in other countries. There are museums to help you learn about anything you want to study.

Why are museums important?

Underline another good title for this story.

Preserved Animals

Famous People

What Is a Museum?

Underline the main idea of the story.

There are museums that display things used by people in other countries.

Museums are important in teaching us about life and art forms of the past.

Original works of art can be found in museums.

Match.

original — protect; save; keep from spoiling

preserve — particularly; mainly

display — not a copy

especially — exhibit; reveal; show

Circle.

(T) F   Museums help people study the past.

T (F) Museums only display things used by people in their own country.

Check the two that apply.

Original things . . .

√ may be old.

√ are real.

X are copies.

X were never used.

What is a hall of fame?

A hall of fame is a special kind of museum. A hall of fame honors famous people. The people honored in a hall of fame are alike in some way. They may all have been inventors, musicians, or may have lived in the same part of the country. There are many kinds of halls of fame. The National Baseball Hall of Fame, the National Hall of Fame for American Indians, and the Senate Hall of Fame are just three of the many halls of fame.

The Hall of Fame for Great Americans was the first hall of fame. It was built in New York in 1900. It was built to honor Americans who did very important things for the United States of America. Busts (statues of the head and shoulder) are on display.

What is a hall of fame?

Underline another good title for this story.

A Hall of Fame

Great Americans

New York's Hall of Fame

Underline the main idea of the story.

The Hall of Fame for Great Americans is in New York.

Busts of famous Americans are in many halls of fame.

A hall of fame is a special kind of museum to
honor famous people.

Match.

display — someone who thinks out or produces something for the first time

inventor — formally recognized; show great respect for

honor — to put on view; to show

museum — a place for keeping or showing a collection of things

Circle.

T (F) There is only one hall of fame.

(T) F Famous people are honored in a hall of fame.

(T) F A hall of fame is a kind of museum.

Check the two that apply.

The Hall of Fame for Great Americans . . .

✓ was the first hall of fame.

✗ honors famous car drivers.

✓ is in New York.

What is a block party?

Sometimes the people who live on the same block have a party. Everyone in that neighborhood is invited. The street is blocked off. Then there is not any traffic. People can use the street for playing games and setting up picnic tables. Everyone brings a lot of food. There may even be a big barbecue. There are many cold things to drink.

Sometimes people cool cans and bottles of drinks in big tubs filled with ice. Usually there is music for dancing. Some block parties have a band. Sometimes someone just turns a stereo (record player) on real loud. Everyone has a good time. The children may play until it gets dark. Block parties last until very late. When they are over, everyone is tired and happy.

Underline another good title for this story.

Going on a Picnic

<u>A Party in the Street</u>

Games Children Play

Underline the main idea of the story.

<u>A block party is a day of fun, games, and food for the people in the neighborhood.</u>

There is no traffic allowed on the street during a block party.

There is a lot to eat and drink at a block party.

Match.

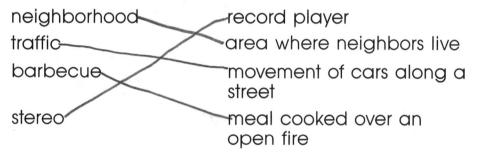

neighborhood — record player

traffic — area where neighbors live

barbecue — movement of cars along a street

stereo — meal cooked over an open fire

Circle.

(T) F   A street is blocked off when people have a block party.

T (F) Block parties end when it gets dark.

(T) F   A block party is for people who live on a certain block.

Check the two that apply.

A block party . . .

✓ is a neighborhood party.

___ is held in a school yard.

✓ is for town or city neighbors.

___ is for country neighbors.

What is a fair?

A fair is a place where people show things that they have made or grown. The things that they show are called exhibits. People come from many places to show things. There are hundreds of kinds of exhibits. You can see anything from pickles to cows to lace tablecloths to tractor engines. Sometimes there are prizes for the people who bring the best exhibits. People come from many places to see the exhibits. People learn from the exhibits. Some exhibits show how to make things.

Some fairs have carnival rides. They have many places where people can buy food. Some fairs have games and contests.

Underline another good title for this story.

Tractor Engines

<u>Come to the Fair</u>

Games and Contests

Underline the main idea of the story.

Some fairs have carnival rides.

<u>A fair is a place where people exhibit things.</u>

People come from many places to exhibit at fairs.

Match.

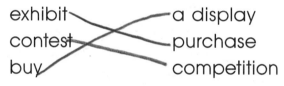

exhibit — a display

contest — purchase

buy — competition

Circle.

T   (F)   A fair is only an animal show.

(T)   F   You can buy things at a fair.

(T)   F   There are many interesting exhibits to see at a fair.

Check the two that apply.

An exhibit . . .

_____ is something to eat.

__✓__ is something that is shown at a fair.

__✓__ is fun for many people to see.

What is an auction?

An auction is a place where certain kinds of things are sold. It is hard for sellers to decide how much to charge for some things. They can sell such things at an auction. Antiques and other used things are sold at auctions. Livestock (farm animals), paintings, and many other kinds of things are sold at auctions. People who want to buy such things go to auctions.

An auctioneer runs the auction. Buyers sit or stand around the auctioneer. The auctioneer puts an item up for sale. People take turns saying how much they will pay for it. This is called bidding. Each person who bids must make a higher bid than the last person. It gets very noisy when many people want to buy the same item. The person who makes the highest bid gets to buy the item. That person is the highest bidder.

Underline another good title for this story.

A Noisy Place

Buying at an Auction

Buying Livestock

Underline the main idea of the story.

An auctioneer is the person who runs the auction.

At an auction, people may buy many kinds of things by bidding for them.

People take turns bidding for the item that's up for sale.

Match.

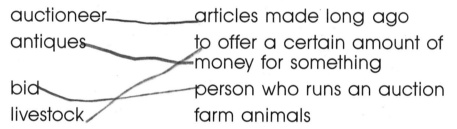

auctioneer — articles made long ago

antiques — to offer a certain amount of money for something

bid — person who runs an auction

livestock — farm animals

Circle.

(T) F   People bid the amount of money they will pay for items at an auction.

T (F)   An auctioneer does the bidding.

Check the two that apply.

Auction items . . .

✓ are sold to the highest bidder.

___ have price tags.

___ are all alike.

✓ include antiques and livestock.

What is a flea market?

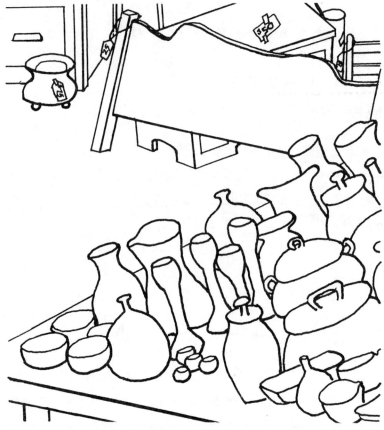

A flea market is a place where people can sell things they no longer need. There are long tables at some flea markets. People can rent a whole table or part of a table. They put their used items on the table. They may put price tags on the items. Items at a flea market do not cost much money.

Used clothes are often sold at flea markets. The owners may have outgrown them, or they may just be tired of them. But the clothes will fit someone else, and they will be new to someone else.

Some people sell homemade crafts at flea markets. Some people sell antiques at flea markets. There are many interesting things to see and buy at a flea market.

Underline another good title for this story.

<u>Selling at the Flea Market</u>

Outgrown Clothes

Making Money

Underline the main idea of the story.

There are long tables at some flea markets.

<u>A flea market is a place where people sell used items.</u>

Some people sell antiques at flea markets.

Match.

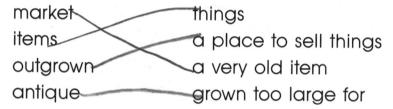

market   things

items   a place to sell things

outgrown   a very old item

antique   grown too large for

Circle.

(T) F   Most people sell new things at a flea market.

T (F)   You can find many interesting things at a flea market.

(T) F   Sometimes people sell outgrown clothing at a flea market.

Check the two that apply.

Flea market items . . .

____ are still usable.

____ are always painted blue.

____ do not cost much money.

Why do some stores have sales?

Sometimes stores have more of some items than they can sell. The store managers want to get rid of these overstocked items. They put the items on sale. If the prices are lower, more people will buy them. Shoppers can save money if they buy things on sale.

Items that are used only one season are called seasonal items. Valentines, garden seeds, and mittens are seasonal items. Seasonal items are put on sale at the end of each season. People do not want to pay full price at the end of the season. Store managers do not want to keep them in the store for another year.

Sales help stores make room for new things. Sales also help bring shoppers into the store. Shoppers come to buy sale items. But they usually buy other things, too.

Why do some stores have sales?

Underline another good title for this story.

Selling for Less

A Store Manager's Job

Seasonal Items

Underline the main idea of the story.

Shoppers can save money by buying things on sale.

Store sales benefit both the store and its shoppers.

Sales help bring shoppers into the store.

Match.

manager	having more than needed of an item.
overstocked	something that is used only during one season
item	person who is in charge of a business
seasonal	an article

Circle.

T   F   Items on sale are free.

T   F   Seasonal items are items that are used only during one season.

T   F   Sale prices are usually very high.

Check the three that apply.

Sales . . .

___ help stores sell overstocked items.

___ help shoppers save money.

___ do not help anyone.

___ bring shoppers into stores.

19

Why do companies give coupons?

Grocery stores advertise by putting coupons in newspapers. They advertise certain products at low coupon prices. Grocery store coupons are usually for flour, sugar, hamburger, milk, eggs, or other things that almost everyone uses. Customers like to save money. They go to stores where they can buy necessary items at special coupon prices. They usually buy many other things at the store, too.

Companies that make grocery products use coupons to advertise their brands or to advertise new products. They print coupons in newspapers and magazines or send them in the mail. These coupons let customers buy a product for a few cents less than the price marked at the grocery store. The company will give the grocery store a refund for each coupon they redeem (turn in). Some coupons say a customer may have a free trial package.

Why do companies give coupons?

Underline another good title for this story.

Free Trial Packages

Grocery Stores

Advertising with Coupons

Underline the main idea of the story.

Companies give coupons to interest people in products, and people use coupons to save money.

Some coupons come in the mail, while others are found in the newspaper.

Customers like to save money.

Match.

advertise	most often
necessary	needed
usually	to turn in coupons
redeem	to call public attention to things for sale

Circle.

T F A coupon is a new product.

T F Coupons are used to advertise new products.

T F Coupons help customers save money.

Check the two that apply.

Coupons . . .

____ help customers advertise.

____ help people save money.

____ help stores get new customers.

What is a tax?

A tax is money that is paid to the government. Governments must pay for many things that all people need. Governments must provide (pay for) hospitals, schools, and fire departments. Governments provide airports, roads, and bridges. Governments use money from taxes to pay for these and many other things.

There are many levels of government. Each level of government must provide certain things. Each level has its own way of collecting taxes. The local level of government levies (charges) property taxes. It sends a bill that says how much tax money people must pay on their land, houses, and other buildings. Some levels of government charge a sales tax when people buy something. The state and national governments also collect income taxes (tax on the money you earn).

Underline another good title for this story.

Property Taxes

Collecting and Using Taxes

Levels of Government

Underline the main idea of the story.

Property taxes are charged by the local level of government.

Airports, roads, and bridges are provided by governments.

Tax is money paid to the government by people; it is used to provide things that people need.

Match.

property	something owned
levies	money received for work or services
income	charges; imposes tax

Circle.

T   F   Governments collect tax money for no real reason.

T   F   Tax is money that is paid to the government.

T   F   Each level of government collects taxes the same way.

Check the two that apply.

Tax money . . .

____ is money paid by the government.

____ is collected by each level of government.

____ does not help anyone.

____ pays for many important things.

What are income tax and sales tax?

    Income tax is tax that people pay on their income. Income is money that someone has "coming in" during the year. Salary is one kind of income. The amount of income tax anyone pays depends on how much income they have. People who make a lot of money pay more tax than people who do not make as much money.

    Sales tax is tax that people pay each time they buy something. Stores must collect a certain number of extra pennies for each dollar people spend. The extra pennies go to the government.

What are income tax and sales tax?

Underline another good title for this story.

The Taxes We Pay

Extra Pennies

Income Taxes

Underline the main idea of the story.

People in our country pay many taxes.

People pay sales tax on things they buy.

Salary is one kind of income.

Match.

income	receive
salary	money paid for work
collect	money coming in

Circle.

T F   People pay income tax on the money they make.

T F   Sales tax is a tax only on sailboats.

Check the two that apply.

People pay . . .

____ income tax to the government.

____ sales tax on cars they buy.

____ tax on the air they breathe.

What are a capital and a capitol?

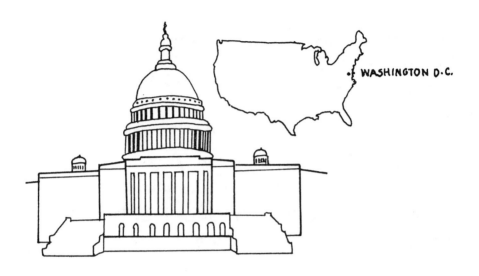

WASHINGTON D.C.

capital — city where a government meets.

capitol — main government building.

Every country has a government. Many people work for the government. These people must meet to make decisions about how their country is run. The city where the government meets is the capital city. Presidents and other government leaders and workers live and work in the capital city.

Capital cities have a capitol building. The capitol building is the main building where government leaders meet. The Congress of the United States meets in the Capitol building in the capital city of Washington, D.C.

Each state in the United States has its own state government. The city where the state government meets is the state capital. There is a state capitol building in each capital city.

What are a capital and a capitol?

Underline another good title for this story.

Capital Cities in the U.S.

Government Capitals and Capitols

The Government of the U.S.

Underline the main idea of the story.

There is a difference between the <u>capital</u> and the <u>capitol</u> of a country or a state.

The capital city of the U.S. is Washington, D.C.

People who work for the government make decisions about how their country is run.

Match.

capital	main government building
leader	judgment or conclusion reached or given
capitol	person who leads or directs
decision	city that is the official meeting place of a government

Check the two that apply.

A capitol . . .

____ is a main government building.

____ is a government city.

____ is the largest city in the state.

____ is located in every capital city.

What is Congress?

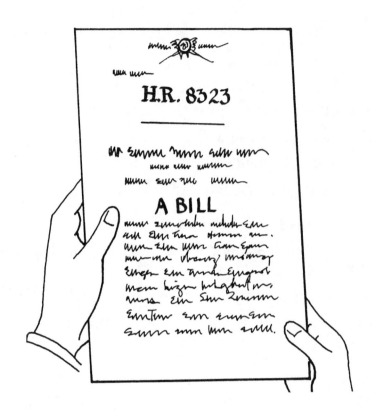

The government makes certain decisions for all of the people. Our country has several branches (parts that work together) of government. Each branch does a special job. The branch of our government that makes laws is Congress. Congress makes laws about many important things.

Each state sends two Senators to Congress. Each state also sends a certain number of Representatives to Congress. Senators and Representatives make decisions about taxes and other things. They try to find out which laws will help people in the state they represent. They try to make laws that will be fair for all people.

Underline another good title for this story.

Senators and Representatives

Congress and Laws

Forty-Eight States

Underline the main idea of the story.

The branch of our government that makes laws is Congress, and each state sends Senators and Representatives to it.

Each state sends two Senators to Congress.

Representatives make decisions about taxes.

Match.

branch	act of deciding
decision	valuable
important	honest
fair	part of the main body

Circle.

T   F   Congress is a branch of government.

T   F   Each state has two Senators.

T   F   Congress is the whole government.

Check the two that apply.

The government . . .

_____ has several branches.

_____ makes firecrackers.

_____ makes decisions for all people.

What is real estate?

Real estate is land and the things that are attached to the land. Buildings and fences are part of real estate. Trees and other plants are part of real estate. Iron, coal, and other valuable things under the soil are part of real estate. But movable things are not part of real estate. Furniture and machines are not part of real estate.

When a person buys a piece of land, he gets a deed. The deed says that he owns the land and other kinds of real estate on the land. If land has a house on it, the house belongs to the new owner. But the furniture in the house still belongs to the old owner. Special agreements have to be made for movable property such as furniture and machines.

What is real estate?

Underline another good title for this story.

What Real Estate Includes

Special Agreements

Movable Property

Underline the main idea of the story.

A deed is what a person receives when he buys a piece of land.

The term real estate includes land and all things that are attached to the land.

Movable property is not part of real estate.

Match.

deed	being of great worth in some way
attached	understanding or arrangement between two or more people.
valuable	an official paper that hands over real estate from one owner to another
agreement	belonging or joined to

Check the two that apply.

Real estate includes . . .

_____ land and other things that are attached to the land.

_____ a deed.

_____ trees and plants.

_____ movable property.

31

What is a deed?

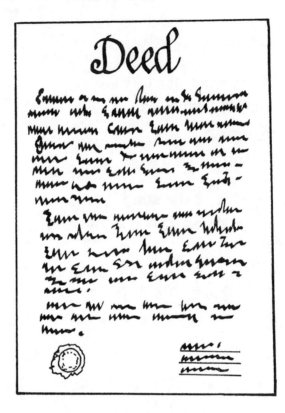

A deed is an official paper that shows who owns a piece of real estate property. Words and numbers on the deed tell exactly where the real estate is located and tells how large the piece of land is.

When a person buys a piece of real estate, he also gets the deed. Both the buyer and the seller must sign the deed in front of some witnesses. They must take an official oath saying that the deed is the real deed. They must also swear that they both understand where the property is located.

The person who buys the land must have the deed recorded. They must make an official record showing that the deed was exchanged lawfully. This is done in the office of the Registrar of Deeds in the county where the land is located.

What is a deed?

Underline another good title for this story.

The Location of Property

Selling Property

Property and Deeds

Underline the main idea of the story.

The buyer and the seller must sign the deed.

A deed is recorded in the office of the Registrar of Deeds.

A deed is an official paper that shows who owns a piece of real estate.

Match.

real estate	promise
witnesses	legally
oath	people who have seen or heard something
lawfully	property

Circle.

T   F   A deed is an official paper.

T   F   A deed tells the size of the land purchased.

T   F   A deed tells who owns a certain piece of real estate.

Check the two that apply.

A person who buys land must . . .

_____ get an official deed from the seller.

_____ sign a secret deed.

_____ have the deed recorded.

33

What is a mobile home?

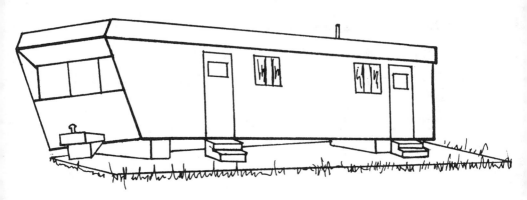

"Mobile" means "movable." A mobile home is a home that was made so that it could be moved. Some mobile homes can be pulled behind a car. But the larger ones must be pulled by a big truck. The widest mobile homes come in two halves. Each half must be pulled separately because a mobile home that is seven meters wide is too wide to be pulled down the road. A mobile home is usually set and anchored on a concrete pad where the owner plans to live.

The inside of a mobile home looks like an apartment. There is a living room, some bedrooms, one or two bathrooms, a dining area, and a kitchen. The kitchen is small, but it has everything that a large kitchen has. Mobile homes usually come with beds, chairs, a table, and living-room furniture.

What is a mobile home?

Underline another good title for this story.

Living in an Apartment

Finding a Mobile Home

A Movable Home

Underline the main idea of the story.

A mobile home is set on a concrete pad.

Mobile homes usually include some furniture when purchased.

A mobile home is a home that can be moved and resembles an apartment.

Match.

separately	hard substance made of sand, gravel, cement, and water
anchor	movable
mobile	individually; one at a time
concrete	hold securely

Circle.

T   F   The inside of a mobile home is quite similar to an apartment.

T   F   A mobile home is built where it is to be used.

T   F   A very large mobile home must be pulled by a truck.

Check the two that apply.

Mobile homes . . .

____ are movable.

____ are anchored to concrete pads.

____ have large kitchens.

35

What is a prefabricated house?

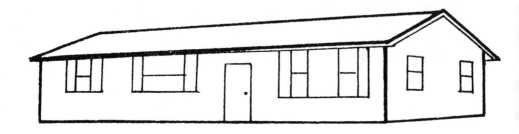

A prefabricated house is built from big pieces made at a factory. Frames for walls and other parts can be built quickly in a factory building. It is also cheaper to build the framework for a house in an indoor factory than to build it on the site.

All of the main pieces for a house are carried on trucks to the site. The pieces for the framework are always carefully labeled. They are made so that they fit together easily. It does not take long for builders to fit a prefabricated house together. Plumbing and wiring are added the same way they are in other houses. Other finishing work is done. When a prefabricated house is finished, it looks like any other kind of house.

What is a prefabricated house?

Underline another good title for this story.

Making a House the Easy Way

Finishing a House

An Inexpensive House

Underline the main idea of the story.

It does not take long for builders to fit a prefabricated house together.

Trucks carry the main pieces for a prefabricated house to the site.

A prefabricated house is built from big pieces made at a factory.

Match.

quickly	plot of land where something is to be located
site	constructed in sections that can be easily shipped and put together
labeled	very fast
prefabricated	marked

Circle.

T   F   A prefabricated house is much more expensive than a regular house.

T   F   Builders fit the prefabricated house together where the house is to stand.

Check the two that apply.

A prefabricated house . . .

____ does not have a frame.

____ looks like any other kind of house.

____ can be put together quickly on the site.

What is a duplex?

A duplex is a house with two apartments. Some duplex apartments are side by side. There is a wall between the two duplex apartments. Some duplex apartments are one on top of the other. Each apartment has its own doors to enter from the outside. Usually, both duplex apartments have the same floor plan (walls and rooms). They share the same yard.

One person owns the duplex home. Usually, the owner lives in one apartment and rents the other to someone else. But sometimes a person or company owns many duplex buildings. They rent out both apartments in each building.

What is a duplex?

Underline another good title for this story.

Owning a Duplex

A Two-Apartment House

Apartment Buildings

Underline the main idea of the story.

Duplex apartments share the same yard.

A duplex is a house with two apartments.

Usually the owner of a duplex lives in one
apartment and rents the other to someone else.

Match.

duplex	person who owns something
apartment	house consisting of two separate apartments
rent	group of rooms to live in
owner	to give temporary use of an apartment in return for payment

Circle.

T F A duplex is the same as an apartment complex.

T F Usually a duplex is owned by one person.

T F A duplex may have two, three, or four small apartments.

Check the two that apply.

A duplex . . .

____ has two apartments.

____ is one big apartment.

____ has an outside door for each apartment.

____has a separate yard for each apartment.

What is a condominium?

A condominium is an apartment that people own instead of rent. Some buildings have only six condominium apartments in them. Other condominium buildings have more than 100 apartments in them. Sometimes there are many condominium apartment buildings together. There may be shops and a small park nearby.

Usually, each person or family who lives in a condominium owns it. They do not pay rent. Instead, they make monthly payments until they have paid for their condominiums. Each condominium owner also pays a maintenance fee. This is money used to pay for taking care of the grounds around the condominium. The maintenance fee pays for taking care of elevators and lobbies. It also pays for other parts of the condominium that everyone uses.

What is a condominium?

Underline another good title for this story.

Maintenance Fees

Living with Others

Owning an Apartment

Underline the main idea of the story.

People who own condominiums must pay a maintenance fee.

A condominium is an apartment that people own instead of rent.

Some condominiums have over 100 apartments in one building.

Match.

usually	most often
lobby	money paid for use of property or services
rent	a building's entryway
maintenance	upkeep

Circle.

T   F   A condominium is a kind of apartment.

T   F   Some condominium buildings are very large.

T   F   Usually, people rent condominiums.

Check the two that apply.

Condominium owners . . .

____ must hire their own gardener.

____ pay a maintenance fee.

____ make monthly payments to buy their home.

____ each buy their own elevator.

Crossword Comprehension Review

Solve this puzzle after you have finished the whole book.

Across

5. During an auction, people take turns saying how much they will pay for an item. What is this called?
6. Original objects are stored and displayed here.
7. The section of a bird's stomach that mashes food and breaks it into small pieces.
8. An apartment that is owned by people instead of rented.
10. A place where antiques and used things are sold by an auctioneer is called an _____.
11. When the environment of an animal changes too much, the animal may become _____.

Down

1. What is an official paper that shows who owns a piece of real estate property?
2. _____ is a branch of our government that makes laws.
3. In the winter, some animals go through a long period of deep sleep called _____.
4. All _____ are warm-blooded animals that have hair, and whose females produce milk.
9. Another tax people pay on any money they have "coming in" during the year is called _____ tax.

Word Bank

property   hibernation   extinct   income

gizzard   museum   bidding   platypus

larvae   Congress   mammals   condominium

auction   migration   deed

How does a snail move?

A snail has a broad, flat foot. A snail's foot is very different from the feet of most other animals. It has no bones. And a snail has only one foot. The part of the snail that touches the ground is its foot.

A gland in the snail's foot makes a slimy liquid. The slimy liquid oozes out of the foot onto the ground. The liquid helps the snail move. It makes a path where the snail can crawl. Many tiny muscles in the foot ripple. The rippling movement pushes back against the slimy path. The snail slides slowly forward.

The slimy liquid also protects the soft foot from injury. A snail can crawl over sharp objects without getting cut.

How does a snail move?

Underline another good title for this story.

A Slimy Liquid

The Movement of a Snail

Muscles in the Foot

Underline the main idea of the story.

A snail's foot has no bones.

A slimy liquid and tiny foot muscles help a snail move.

The slimy liquid protects the snail from sharp objects.

Match.

protect	an organ of the body that makes a special liquid
muscle	safeguard; make safe
slimy	bundles of fibers that produce body movements
gland	slippery and sticky

Circle.

T   F   A snail has just one foot.

T   F   A slimy liquid helps a snail move.

T   F   Snails walk on their six tiny feet.

Check the two that apply.

A snail's foot . . .

___ has many tiny muscles.

___ has a special gland.

___ does not touch the ground.

___ has three bones in it.

45

Why do squirrels have bushy tails?

There are many species (kinds) of squirrels. Most species of squirrels live on the ground. Ground squirrels do not have bushy tails.

A few species of squirrels that live in trees have bushy tails. Tree squirrels run quickly from branch to branch. They use their bushy tails to help them keep their balance as they jump from one branch to another. Squirrels use their tails to help them jump smoothly and safely. Squirrels curl up in a ball when they sleep. Their tails help keep them and their babies warm.

Why do squirrels have bushy tails?

Underline another good title for this story.

How Squirrels Use Their Tails

Animal Shelters

Keeping Your Balance

Underline the main idea of the story.

The tail of a tree squirrel helps it keep its balance.

Most squirrels live on the ground.

Squirrels jump from one branch to another.

Match.

bushy	stability; steadiness
balance	thick and spreading out like a bush
species	a distinct kind of plant or animal

Circle.

T   F   All squirrels have bushy tails.

T   F   Most species of squirrels live on the ground.

Check the two that apply.

Tree squirrels use their tails . . .

___ to help them keep their balance.

___ to keep them warm.

___ like a fan.

Can some fish really fly?

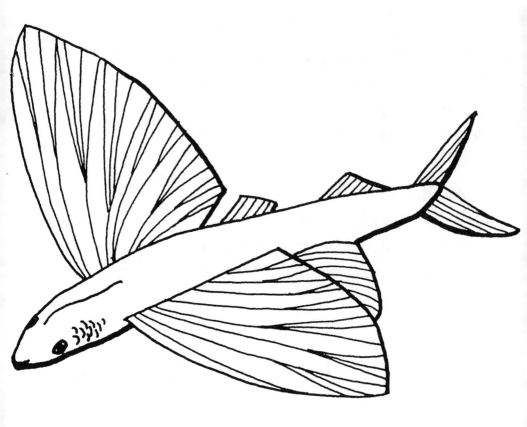

There are many species (kinds) of fish called flying fish. These species of fish seem to fly for short distances. But flying fish really only glide through the air. They cannot fly like birds can fly.

Flying fish have large pectoral fins. The pectoral fins are folded against the sides of the fish when it swims. Flying fish usually swim near the surface (top) of the water. They use their strong tail muscles to throw themselves out of the water. Then they spread their big pectoral fins out like the wings of a glider. A flying fish can stay in the air for several seconds. Then it glides smoothly back into the water.

Can some fish really fly?

Underline another good title for this story.

Flying Fish

How Birds Fly

Where Fish Live

Underline the main idea of the story.

Flying fish have strong tail muscles.

Flying fish swim near the surface of the water.

Some fish seem to fly through the air.

Match.

glide	top
surface	move smoothly through the air
several	normally
usually	more than two

Circle.

T   F   Several kinds of fish can really fly like birds.

T   F   Flying fish have wings.

T   F   Flying fish have special side fins.

Check the three that apply.

Flying fish . . .

____ can fly many kilometers.

____ have large pectoral fins.

____ have strong tail muscles.

____ glide but do not fly.

____ swim near the bottom of the sea.

What are mammals?

Mammals are a class (main group) of animals. There are thousands of different kinds of mammals. Bats, lions, and human beings are just three kinds of mammals. Mammals are alike in certain ways. Here are some ways they are alike:

All mammals must breathe air.

All mammals are warm-blooded.

Most mammals have exactly four limbs (legs and arms).

All mammals have some hair.

Most young mammals grow inside the body of the mother.

All female mammals produce milk to feed their young (babies).

What are mammals?

COMPREHENSION ACTIVITIES

Underline another good title for this story.

Warm-Blooded Animals

Common Characteristics of Mammals

The Air We Breathe

Underline the main idea of the story.

There are many different kinds of mammals.

Man is a mammal.

All mammals are alike in certain ways.

Match.

produce	main group
limb	a person
class	an arm, leg, or wing
human being	to make or manufacture

Circle.

T F   Most mammals lay eggs.

T F   Cows, ducks, and horses are all mammals.

Check the two that apply.

Mammals . . .

___ are cold-blooded.

___ may have six legs.

___ have hair.

___ feed milk to their young.

The Homework Booklet IF0144

Copyright 1987, Instructional Fair, Inc.

What do warm-blooded and cold-blooded mean?

The body of a warm-blooded animal makes body heat. The body of a warm-blooded animal is always about the same temperature. The body of a warm-blooded animal stays warm even when the outside air is very cold. All mammals and all birds are warm-blooded. The hair of mammals and the feathers of birds help them keep their body heat.

Cold-blooded animals cannot make body heat. Cold-blooded animals are about the same temperature as the outside air. Reptiles, fish, amphibians, and insects are some classes (main groups) of cold-blooded animals. All animals except mammals and birds are cold-blooded.

What do warm-blooded and cold-blooded mean?

(final)

What do warm-blooded and cold-blooded mean?

COMPREHENSION ACTIVITIES

Underline another good title for this story.

Feathers of Birds

Warm and Cold-Blooded Animals

Reptiles, Fish, and Amphibians

Underline the main idea of the story.

All mammals are warm-blooded.

Warm-blooded animals produce their own body heat and cold-blooded animals do not.

Reptiles are cold-blooded animals.

Match.

protected   cold-blooded animals

reptiles   guarded

temperature   main groups

classes   measure of hotness or coldness

Circle.

T   F   Cold-blooded animals are always cold.

T   F   Warm-blooded animals make their own body heat.

Check the two that apply.

Warm-blooded animals . . .

____ have the same body temperature as the outside air.

____ make their own body heat.

____ are always about the same temperature.

Is the platypus really a mammal?

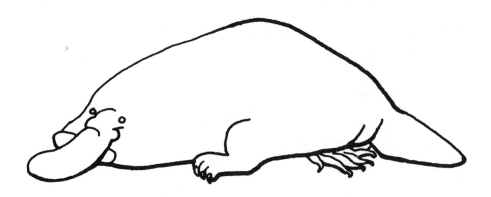

The platypus is a mammal because it has fur and feeds milk to its young (babies). But the platypus is different from most other mammals in some ways. The platypus does not grow live young inside its body. It lays eggs instead. A platypus has milk glands and feeds its young milk. The platypus is warm-blooded. But its body temperature changes several degrees with the weather.

The platypus is very different from most other mammals. The platypus is in the monotreme group. A monotreme is a mammal that lays eggs. The platypus and the echidna are the only monotremes. They are the only mammals that lay eggs.

Is the platypus really a mammal?

Underline another good title for this story.

Milk Glands

A Mammal That Lays Eggs

The Body Temperature of a Mammal

Underline the main idea of the story.

A platypus is different from most other mammals in some ways.

A platypus has milk glands.

An echidna is an egg-laying mammal.

Match.

young	a mammal that lays eggs
nurse	to nourish; feed
mammals	group of animals that produce milk to feed their young
monotreme	offspring; baby

Circle.

T F The platypus is a monotreme.

T F The platypus is cold-blooded.

T F A monotreme is a mammal that lays eggs.

Check the three that apply.

The platypus . . .

____ is a mammal.

____ produces milk.

____ lays eggs.

____ is cold-blooded.

55

Are whales really mammals?

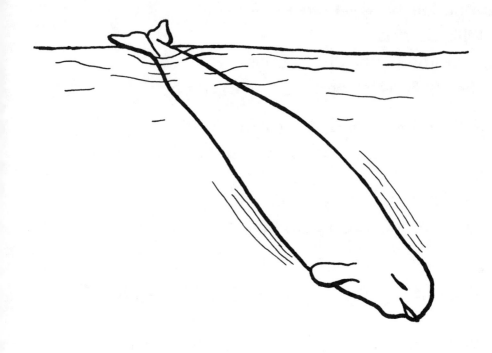

Whales look very much like fish. Whales live in the sea. But whales are not fish. Whales are mammals. Whales breathe air. Whales are warm-blooded. Female whales give birth to live young. Female whales produce milk to feed their young.

But whales are very different from most other mammals. Whales have almost no hair. And they have flippers instead of front legs. They do not have back flippers or legs. But a whale has small hipbones where other mammals have their back legs. Scientists think that the whale used to have legs where the small bones are now.

Are whales really mammals?

Underline another good title for this story.

A Whale's Flippers

Whales Are Mammals

Baby Whales

Underline the main idea of the story.

Whales have very little hair.

Whales breathe air.

Whales are different from other mammals.

Match.

produce	warm-blooded animals that have hair and whose females produce milk for their young
mammals	the ocean
sea	to bring forth

Circle.

T   F   Whales are warm-blooded.

T   F   Female whales lay eggs.

T   F   Whales are fish.

Check the two that apply.

A whale . . .

____ is a mammal that lives in the sea.

____ must breathe air.

____ has back flippers.

How are all birds alike?

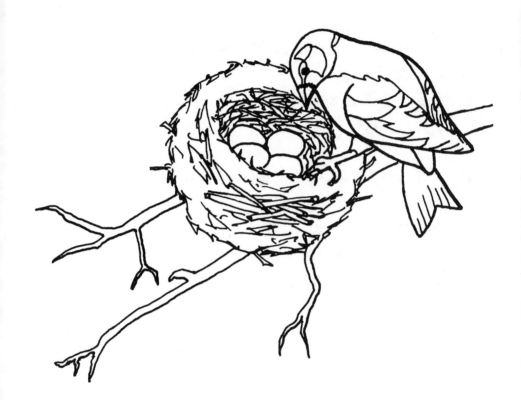

Birds form one class (main group) of animals. All birds are alike in some ways. All birds have feathers. And birds are the only animals that have feathers. All birds have a hard mouth called a beak. Birds do not have teeth. All birds have two wings, two legs, and two feet.

Wings make it possible for birds to fly. Birds also have hollow bones and lightweight internal organs. These characteristics help birds to fly, too. Almost all birds can fly. There are a few birds that cannot fly. Six flightless birds are the penguin, the kiwi, the ostrich, the rhea, the cassoway, and the emu.

All birds lay eggs. Almost all birds build some type of nest. Adult birds take care of young birds for a while after they hatch.

How are all birds alike?

Underline another good title for this story.

Hollow-Boned Animals

Common Characteristics of Birds

Beaks

Underline the main idea of the story.

Wings and lightweight internal organs make it possible for birds to fly.

Birds form one group of animals that have common identifying features.

There are six kinds of birds that cannot fly.

Match.

hollow	having a space within
flightless	a bird's mouth
beak	not able to fly

Circle.

T   F   All birds have feathers.

T   F   Birds are mammals.

T   F   All birds can fly.

Check the three that apply.

Birds . . .

____ have hollow bones.

____ have teeth.

____ lay eggs.

____ take care of their young.

Why don't birds have teeth?

Birds do not have teeth because they can swallow their food whole. Birds have stomachs that are made for grinding up food.

Everything that a bird eats is stored in its crop. When the stomach is ready for it, the food is passed into the first part of the stomach. The food is softened there by strong, digestive juices. The food then moves to the second part of the stomach, called the gizzard. The gizzard mashes the food and breaks it into small pieces. This process does the job that our "chewing" does.

When a bird eats, it picks up pebbles and sand along with the food. The sharp edges of the pebbles and sand also help to break up the food.

Underline another good title for this story.

How Birds Digest Their Food

Pebbles and Sand

What Birds Eat

Underline the main idea of the story.

A bird eats pebbles.

Birds grind up food in their stomachs.

There are digestive juices in the stomach.

Match.

gizzard	special body liquids that help change food into a form that can be used by the body
crop	place where a bird stores food until the stomach is ready for it
digestive juices	section of a bird's stomach that grinds up food

Circle.

T   F   Birds eat pebbles with their food.

T   F   The crop is a place where a bird stores food.

T   F   Birds have small teeth called crops.

Check the two that apply.

A gizzard . . .

____ mashes food that birds eat.

____ is a part of a bird's stomach.

____ is a kind of bird.

____ stores the bird's food.

What is migration?

Many animals move from one place to another in order to find better living conditions. This is called migration. Many animals spend winter in one place and summer in another. They move from north to south and from south to north as the seasons change. That way, they can spend the winter where it is warm. They will usually be able to find more food there, too. Some animals migrate from one climatic (weather) zone to another in the same hemisphere (half of the earth). Some animals migrate from one hemisphere to the other.

Scientists do not know what causes animals to migrate. Some scientists think that temperature changes cause changes in the animals' bodies. Some scientists think that shortages in certain kinds of foods cause animals to migrate.

Underline another good title for this story.

Food Shortages

Moving For Better Living Conditions

The Changing of the Seasons

Underline the main idea of the story.

Shortages of food can cause animals to migrate.

Animals migrate in order to find better living conditions.

Animals can migrate from one hemisphere to another.

Match.

migrate	spring, summer, winter, fall
seasons	deficiency; lack of
hemispheres	to move from one place to another in order to find better living conditions
shortage	halves of the earth

Check the two that apply.

Animals migrate . . .

____ so they can find food.

____ when the seasons change.

____ when they feel like taking a vacation.

What is hibernation?

Hibernation is a long period of very deep sleep. Some kinds of ground squirrels, woodchucks, and other animals hibernate during the winter. They hibernate because there is not enough available food during the winter.

When it is time for an animal to hibernate, it finds a sheltered place to stay, such as a cave or a burrow. When an animal hibernates, its body temperature gets very low. But the animal does not freeze. While hibernating, the animal does not need to eat. It breathes very slowly. An animal that is hibernating seems almost as if it were dead. It will not warm up and wake up completely until spring. In the spring, there will be plenty of food for it to eat.

What is hibernation?

Underline another good title for this story.

How Animals Hibernate

Springtime

Food in Winter

Underline the main idea of the story.

Hibernating animals wake up in the spring.

Hibernation is a long period of very deep sleep that some animals enter during the winter.

Animals do not eat when they are hibernating.

Match.

plenty	time
hibernate	very deep sleep
period	a lot

Circle.

T   F   Some animals hibernate during the summer.

T   F   An animal dies when it hibernates.

Check the two that apply.

A hibernating animal . . .

____ becomes cold and wakes up.

____ freezes.

____ does not eat.

____ breathes slowly.

What is a rattlesnake's rattle made of?

A young rattlesnake has one hard cap on its tail. The cap is made of a hard material. The hard cap does not come off when the rattlesnake sheds its skin. In fact, each time a rattlesnake grows a new skin, a new cap is added to the end of the snake's tail. A rattlesnake's rattle is made of these hard, hollow caps. The edges of the caps look like rings on the rattlesnake's tail.

Some people think the rings on the rattle tell the age of the snake. This is not true. A new ring is added each time the snake sheds its skin. But a rattlesnake sheds its skin more than once a year. Also, some of the rings may have broken off.

What is a rattlesnake's rattle made of?

Underline another good title for this story.

Poisonous Snakes

The Rattle of the Rattlesnake

How to Tell the Age of a Snake

Underline the main idea of the story.

A rattlesnake sheds its skin more than once a year.

The rattlesnake's rattle develops as the snake develops and grows.

Telling the age of a snake by the rings on its tail is not accurate.

Match.

shed   cover; top part

rattle   throw off

cap   set of hard, hollow caps at the end of a rattlesnake's tail used to make sharp, short sounds.

Check the three that apply.

A rattlesnake . . .

_____ gets only one cap each year.

_____ sheds its skin more than once a year.

_____ has one hard cap on its tail when it is young.

_____ has a rattle made of hard material.

67

Are snakes useful?

Many people do not like snakes at all. They are afraid that snakes will bite them. Some people try to kill every snake they see. But there are only four kinds of snakes in North America that are dangerous to people. These four snakes are poisonous. The poisonous snakes are coral snakes, water moccasins, copperheads, and rattlesnakes. People should learn what they look like.

There are dozens of kinds of snakes in North America. Most kinds of snakes are really very useful animals. Most snakes eat mice, rats, insects, and other small animals. Mice and rats eat a lot of grain. Mice, rats, and insects destroy a lot of food. They also carry certain disease germs. Snakes help people by eating some of these pests.

Underline another good title for this story.

Coral Snakes

How Snakes Help Man

Mice, Rats, and Insects

Underline the main idea of the story.

Some people are afraid of snakes.

Mice and rats eat grain.

Most snakes are useful.

Match.

dangerous	a destructive small animal
dozen	spoil; ruin
destroy	harmful
pest	twelve

Circle.

T   F   Most snakes are not poisonous.

T   F   There are many kinds of snakes.

T   F   Most snakes are useful.

Check the two that apply.

People should . . .

____ kill all snakes.

____ learn about snakes.

____ bite snakes.

____ know which snakes are poisonous.

What are insects?

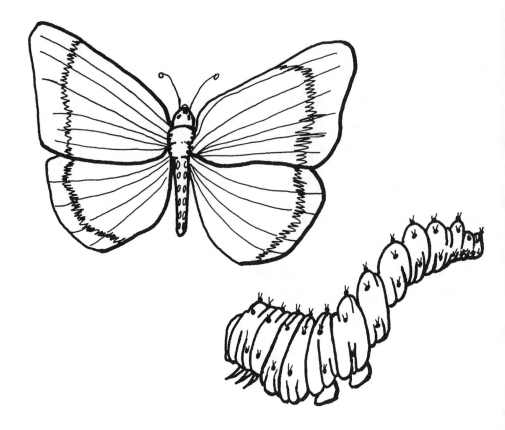

　　Insects form one class (group) of small animals. There are many kinds of insects. Some kinds are very different from other kinds. Some insects can fly. Some insects live in water. Some insects live underground. Some insects are almost too small to be seen. Some insects are bigger than mice. But all insects are alike in some ways. All insects lay eggs. Insect eggs hatch into larvae. The larvae look like worms. The larvae grow and change until they are adult insects. All adult insects have six legs. All adult insects have three-part bodies. Many kinds of insects have wings. Insects that have wings may have two wings or four wings. Insects have antennae (feelers). Insects smell with their antennae.

Underline another good title for this story.

What Are Antennae?

Laying Eggs

Information on Insects

Underline the main idea of the story.

All insects lay eggs that hatch into larvae.

Although there are many different kinds of insects, all insects are alike in some ways.

There are insects of all sizes.

Match.

hatch   feelers; sense organs

larvae   an animal or plant that is grown up

antennae   to bring forth from eggs

adult   wormlike form of newly hatched insects

Circle.

T   F   Insects form one class of small animals.

T   F   All insects live underground.

Check the two that apply.

Insects . . .

____ may be as big as dogs.

____ may have four wings.

____ may have eight legs.

____ have antennae.

Why is some fruit wormy?

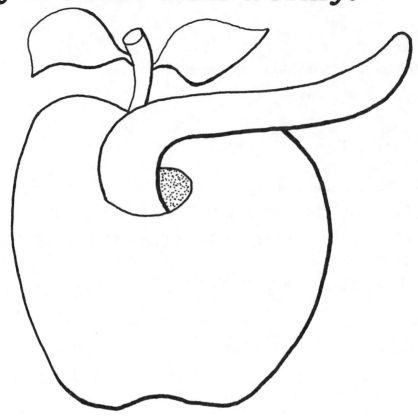

Some pieces of fruit have what looks like worms in them. But these really are not worms. They are the larvae of certain kinds of flies. The adult female flies lay eggs in fruit. These kinds of flies have sharp, hollow egg-laying tubes. The female fly jabs the fruit with the tube. Then she lays an egg through the tube.

Larvae hatch from the eggs. The larvae spend all of their time eating and growing. They eat tunnels through the fruit. Later, each larva forms a hard skin around itself. It goes through change inside the hard skin, and eventually, the larva becomes an adult fly.

Why is some fruit wormy?

Underline another good title for this story.

Growing Fruit

Fruit and Larvae

Adult Flies

Underline the main idea of the story.

Female flies have sharp, hollow tubes for laying their eggs.

The larvae of flies sometime grow in fruit.

The larva forms a hard skin around itself.

Match.

skin	wormlike form of a newly hatched insect
hatch	outer layer
larva	come out of an egg

Check the three that apply.

The larvae in fruit . . .

____ are worms.

____ hatch from eggs.

____ are fly larvae.

____ eat the fruit.

How can earthworms breathe underground?

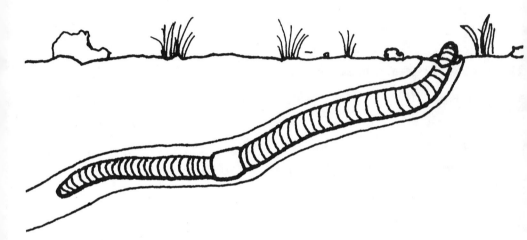

There is little or no air deep under the surface of the earth. But earthworms do not dig very deeply under the earth's surface. Earthworms live in the topsoil near the surface of the earth. There is a lot of air in the topsoil. The air is between the soil particles.

Earthworms dig tunnels as they move through the topsoil. Air flows easily through the tunnels that the earthworms dig. When it rains, the tunnels are filled with water. Air cannot flow into the tunnels when they are filled with water. Then the earthworms come to the surface of the soil.

How can earthworms breathe underground?

Underline another good title for this story.

The Earth's Surface

How Earthworms Get Air

The Topsoil

Underline the main idea of the story.

Tunnels fill with water during a rain.

There is a lot of air in the topsoil.

Earthworms get air from the topsoil and from the tunnels they dig.

Match.

surface	the surface layer of soil
topsoil	very small pieces
particles	an underground passage
tunnel	top

Circle.

T   F   Earthworms do not need air at all.

T   F   Earthworms live deep underground.

T   F   Air flows deep into the surface of the earth.

Check the three that apply.

There is air . . .

____ deep underground.

____ near the surface of the earth.

____ between topsoil particles.

____ in water-filled tunnels.

____ in tunnels that earthworms dig.

    75

What are spiders?

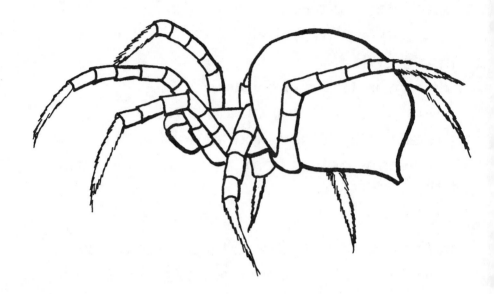

Spiders are a small kind of animal. Most spiders spin webs. Some people think spiders are insects. This is not true. Spiders have eight legs, not just six. Eight-legged animals are called arachnids. Spiders are arachnids.

Spiders have two-part bodies. The front part has the brain, eyes, mouth, fangs, and legs. The back part has the stomach, lungs, heart, and other parts. Spiders have spinnerettes. Spiders use spinnerettes to spin webs. All of a spider's web-making parts are in the back part of the spider.

A female spider makes a silky sac. She lays hundreds of eggs in the sac. One tiny spider hatches from each egg. (Spiders do not have a larval stage.) The tiny spiders stay in the sac for a few days. Some kinds of female spiders take care of their young after they hatch.

What are spiders?

Underline another good title for this story.

The Larval Stage

All About Spiders

How to Spin Webs

Underline the main idea of the story.

Spiders lay their eggs in a silky sac.

Spiders use spinnerettes to make webs.

Spiders are arachnids and have different characteristics than insects.

Match.

arachnid	a long, sharp tooth
fang	animal with eight legs and a two-part body
spinnerette	fine; soft; smooth
silky	used in spinning threads of silk

Circle.

T   F   Spiders are arachnids.

T   F   Spiders have spinnerettes.

T   F   Arachnids are the same as insects.

Check the two that apply.

Spiders . . .

____ are insects.

____ have two-part bodies.

____ have eight legs.

Can a spider get stuck in its own web?

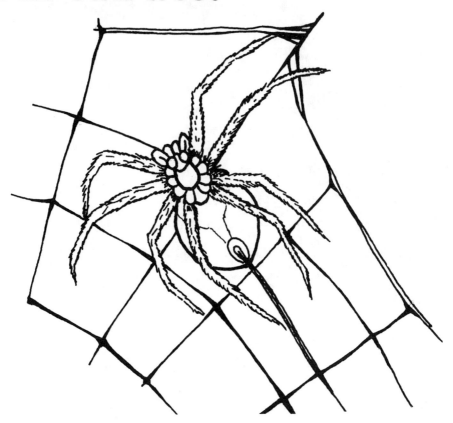

A spider's body makes a liquid called silk. A spider spins its web from liquid silk. The silk is liquid when it comes out of the spinnerettes. Air dries the liquid. The liquid silk becomes a strong thread.

A spider's body makes two main kinds of silk. One kind of silk is sticky. The other is not. The spider makes the first part of the web of non-sticky silk. Then it adds the strands of sticky silk. Insects get caught on the sticky silk.

The spider has a special, hooked claw on each foot. It uses the claws to walk on the threads. The spider does not get caught in its own web.

Can a spider get stuck in its own web?

Underline another good title for this story.

Spiders and Their Silk

A Spider's Home

Many Kinds of Silk

Underline the main idea of the story.

A spider's body makes silk.

Spiders make sticky silk.

Insects get caught on the sticky silk, but a spider has a special hooked claw on each foot which helps it to walk on the silk threads.

Match.

liquid   adhesive; clinging

strong   able to flow, like water

sticky   tough; durable

Circle.

T F Spiders make two kinds of silk thread.

T F Spiders often get stuck in their own webs.

Check the two that apply.

Spiders . . .

____ can walk on silk strands because of their special hooked claws.

____ make two main kinds of silk.

____ often catch people in their webs.

____ like to catch dogs in their webs.

Why do some species become extinct?

Each species of plant or animal does best in a certain environment. Each species of plant or animal needs certain things in order to survive (live and reproduce itself).

Our world is always changing. It changes naturally (without people causing it). Many plants and animals become extinct when their environment has changed too much. This is natural extinction. This kind of extinction cannot be stopped. New kinds of plants and animals have had time to develop. They can take the place of the extinct species.

But people also change the environment. People cause pollution. Pollution changes the environment. Cutting down forests changes the environment. There are many things that people do that change the environment. Many changes that people make cause living things to become extinct.

Why do some species become extinct?

Underline another good title for this story.

Our Changing World and Extinction

New Plants and Animals

Forests

Underline the main idea of the story.

Cutting down forests changes the environment.

Plants need certain foods.

Plants and animals will die if there are large changes in their environments.

Match.

survive	no longer living; having died out
reproduce	surroundings
extinct	to remain alive
environment	to produce offspring

Check the two that apply.

People . . .

___ can change the environment.

___ cause pollution.

___ are extinct.

What was the dodo?

    The dodo was a kind of bird. Dodos were about as big as turkeys. Dodos had a big, thick beak. They had short, heavy legs. Dodos had small wings. And they could not fly. Dodos lived on some islands in the Indian Ocean. They had few natural enemies.

    In the early 1600's, explorers began going to the islands where the dodos lived. The dodos were not afraid of people. It was easy for the explorers to catch them. They ate many of the dodos. The explorers brought hogs and dogs to the islands. The hogs and dogs ate the dodos' eggs. There were few young dodos to replace the ones that were killed. Dodos began to die out. The dodo became extinct in 1681.

What was the dodo?

Underline another good title for this story.

Dodo Birds

Early Explorers

Living in the Indian Ocean

Underline the main idea of the story.

Dodos were large, non-flying birds that became extinct.

In the early 1600's, men began exploring the islands in the Indian Ocean.

Dodos and turkeys were about the same size.

Match.

island	a person who investigates an unknown region
explorer	a body of land not as large as a continent, surrounded by water.
Indian Ocean	a large bird, now extinct
dodo	an ocean south of Asia, between Africa and Australia

Check the two that apply.

Dodos . . .

___ are extinct.

___ were very little birds.

___ could fly.

___ were a kind of bird.

83

Wordsearch Vocabulary Review

Solve this wordsearch after you have finished the whole book.

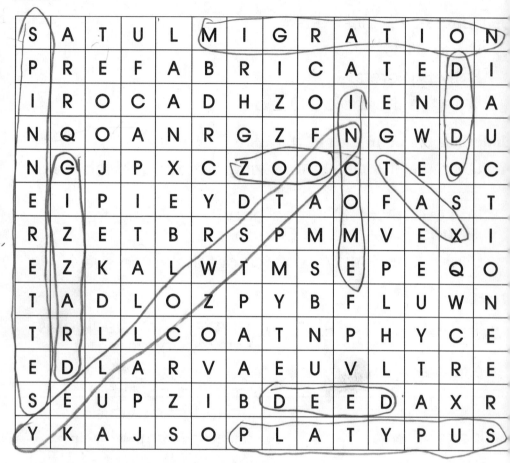

S	A	T	U	L	M	I	G	R	A	T	I	O	N
P	R	E	F	A	B	R	I	C	A	T	E	D	I
I	R	O	C	A	D	H	Z	O	I	E	N	O	A
N	Q	O	A	N	R	G	Z	F	N	G	W	D	U
N	G	J	P	X	C	Z	O	O	C	T	E	O	C
E	I	P	I	E	Y	D	T	A	O	F	A	S	T
R	Z	E	T	B	R	S	P	M	M	V	E	X	I
E	Z	K	A	L	W	T	M	S	E	P	E	Q	O
T	A	D	L	O	Z	P	Y	B	F	L	U	W	N
T	R	L	L	C	O	A	T	N	P	H	Y	C	E
E	D	L	A	R	V	A	E	U	V	L	T	R	E
S	E	U	P	Z	I	B	D	E	E	D	A	X	R
Y	K	A	J	S	O	P	L	A	T	Y	P	U	S

These vocabulary words are from your stories. Find and circle them in the wordsearch.

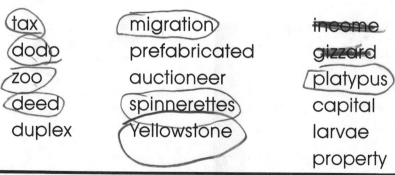

tax	migration	income
dodo	prefabricated	gizzard
zoo	auctioneer	platypus
deed	spinnerettes	capital
duplex	Yellowstone	larvae
		property